GRADE
1

The 2005–2007 Syllabus shoul[d] requirements, especially those f[or] sight-reading. Attention should Notices on the inside front cover, any changes.

The syllabus is obtainable from music retailers or from the Services Department, The Associated Board of the Royal Schools of Music, 24 Portland Place, London W1B 1LU, United Kingdom (please send a stamped addressed C5 (162mm × 229mm) envelope).

In exam centres outside the UK, information and syllabuses may be obtained from the Local Representative.

CONTENTS

Where appropriate, pieces in this volume have been checked with [origin]al source material and edited as necessary for instructional purposes. Fing[ering,] phrasing, bowing, metronome marks and the editorial realization of ornaments (where given) are for guidance only; they are not comprehensive or obligatory.

DO NOT
PHOTOCOPY
© MUSIC

Alternative pieces for this grade

Music origination by Andrew Jones.
Cover by Økvik Design.
Printed in England by Caligraving Ltd, Thetford, Norfolk.

A:1 Robin is to the Greenwood Gone

Arranged by
Edward Huws Jones

ANON. ENGLISH

Robin is to the Greenwood Gone is a popular song from the time of Queen Elizabeth I. Some of the most celebrated composers of the period arranged it for their instrument, including Giles Farnaby for virginals and John Dowland for lute. The tune has a wistful quality, but don't play it too slowly. EHJ

J'ai du bon tabac

Arranged by
Paul de Keyser

ANON. FRENCH

Written around 1760 and attributed to Abbot Charles de l'Attaignant, canon of Rheims, *J'ai du bon tabac* (which begins with the line 'I've got good tobacco in my snuffbox') was a French political song satirizing judges, financiers and well-known figures of the time.

Reproduced from *Violin Playtime*, Book 2, by permission of the publishers. All enquiries for this piece apart from the exams should be addressed to Faber Music Ltd, 3 Queen Square, London WC1N 3AU.

A:3

Minuet

K. 315g No. 7

Arranged by
Sheila Nelson

MOZART

A French dance in triple time, the minuet was popular in aristocratic society from the mid-17th century to the late 18th.

AB 3001

Ode to Joy

from Symphony No. 9, Op. 125

B:1

Arranged by
Edward Huws Jones

BEETHOVEN

This glorious melody was originally written for choir, so enjoy singing it as well as playing it on your violin. Play with lots of bow and make a full sound. If you are performing the piece in a concert, you will want to play it at least twice through (though it should only be played once in the exam). EHJ

B:2

Première valse

CARSE

Adam Carse, a professor of harmony and counterpoint at the Royal Academy of Music, 1922–40, is perhaps best-known for his study of the history of instruments and the orchestra. In 1947 he donated his collection of around 350 historic wind instruments to the Horniman Museum, London.

© 1915, 1994 Stainer & Bell Ltd

Reproduced from *Classic Carse*, Book 1, by permission. All enquiries for this piece apart from the exams should be addressed to Stainer & Bell Ltd, 23 Gruneisen Road, London N3 1DZ.

Celtic Song

No. 2 from *Highland Fling*

B:3

PETER MARTIN

Peter Martin has written and arranged a large number of pieces for young string players. *Highland Fling* is a collection of three pieces, all of which have a distinctly Scottish flavour.

AB 3001

Hora

Arranged by
Paul de Keyser

ANON. BULGARIAN

The *hora* is a traditional dance form found in Bulgaria, Romania, former Yugoslavia and Russia. The dancers form a circle and repeat a sequence of steps which causes the circle to rotate. As with all dance music, the underlying pulse needs to be rock-steady throughout.

Fiddle Time

No. 47 from *Fiddle Time Joggers*

KATHY AND DAVID BLACKWELL

Fiddle Time Joggers is a lively collection of pieces for beginners. Saying the title of this piece twice will fit the rhythm of the first bar, and many other bars too. Try to make the first section loud and lively to contrast with the quiet and legato middle section. Enjoy! K & DB

C:3

Garden

No. 26 from *The Microjazz Violin Collection 1*

CHRISTOPHER NORTON

In a flowing 3/4, *Garden* is jazz-influenced and would benefit from a sweet-toned, very legato style of playing. Start really *piano* – you need to have enough in reserve to get to a real *forte* by b. 19, where a relatively sudden rush of emotion is compensated for by the ritenuto in bb. 27 and 28. It's as though things have got rather intense and need to be reined back! The piano part should be soft-edged and round-toned throughout so as to provide warm, sympathetic support. CN
The square-bracketed metronome mark is suggested for exam purposes.

Checklist of Scales and Arpeggios

Candidates and teachers may find this checklist useful in learning the requirements of the grade. Full details of the forms of the various requirements, including details of rhythms, starting notes and bowing patterns, are given in the syllabus and in the scale books published by the Board.

Grade 1

			separate bows						slurred					
									two quavers to a bow					
Major Scales	D Major	1 Octave												
	A Major	1 Octave												
	G Major	2 Octaves												
									not applicable					
Major Arpeggios	D Major	1 Octave												
	A Major	1 Octave												
	G Major	2 Octaves												